THE COMPL DIET PLAN COOKBOOK

"A Step by Step Guide to Treating PMDD Naturally with Nutritional Secrets and Time-Saving Hacks, a Pre-designed Meal Plan and Recipes and Bonus resources"

Maria L. Kings
Abigail Langley

Table of Contents

IV

Embracing Food as Your Ally on the PMDD Journey

Imagine this: every month, a storm brews within you. Moods swing like a pendulum, fatigue weighs you down like a leaden cloak, and tender feelings bloom into prickly irritability. This, my friend, is the reality of Premenstrual Dysphoric Disorder (PMDD), a hormonal hurricane that can leave you feeling adrift in a sea of discomfort.

But fear not, fellow voyager! There's a hidden compass in this storm, a powerful tool that can help you navigate the choppy waters of PMDD: food. Yes, the very nourishment that fuels your body can be your secret weapon in this battle, a delicious ally that can soothe your symptoms and empower you to reclaim your well-being.

PMDD: A Symphony of Discomfort

PMDD isn't just a bad case of PMS. It's a clinically recognized condition that affects up to 5% of women, unleashing a cascade of physical and emotional symptoms in the days leading up to their period. From the depths of despair to the fiery peaks of anger, it's a rollercoaster ride you didn't sign up for.

Here's a glimpse into the storm:

1. **Emotional upheaval:** Mood swings, irritability, anxiety, and even depression can rear their ugly heads.

2. **Physical woes:** Fatigue, bloating, headaches, and muscle aches can make your body feel like a stranger.

3. **Brain fog and forgetfulness:** Concentration and memory take a backseat, leaving you feeling fuzzy and out of sorts.

4. **Cravings and food sensitivities:** Sugar cravings skyrocket, while certain foods seem to trigger your worst symptoms.

It's a symphony of discomfort, a concerto of chaos that can leave you feeling powerless and misunderstood. But this is where food steps in, ready to harmonize the discord and turn the tide in your favor.

Food: Your Symphony Conductor

Think of your body as an orchestra, and food as the conductor. By choosing the right notes, you can create a harmonious melody that soothes your symptoms and brings balance to your system.

Here's how food can be your champion:

1. **Nutrient power:** Specific vitamins, minerals, and healthy fats can act like calming instruments, reducing inflammation, regulating hormones, and boosting your mood.

2. **Blood sugar balance:** Stable blood sugar levels are crucial for keeping your emotions on an even keel. Food choices that keep your blood sugar in

check will help you avoid the emotional highs and lows.

3. **Brain fuel:** Certain foods nourish your brain cells, improving focus and memory, and helping you navigate the brain fog that often accompanies PMDD.

4. **Mood-boosting magic:** Certain ingredients have natural mood-lifting properties, acting like serotonin serenades that can chase away the blues and bring back your sunshine.

This is just the first movement in your food-fueled symphony of well-being. As we delve deeper into this cookbook, you'll discover a treasure trove of delicious recipes and practical tips that will help you transform your plate into a powerful tool for managing PMDD.

So, take a deep breath, fellow traveler. The storm may rage, but with food as your compass, you can navigate the choppy waters of PMDD and find your way to a calmer, brighter shore. Let's embark on this delicious journey together, one bite at a time!

CHAPTER 1

Understanding PMDD and Nutrition: Demystifying the Food-Mood Connection

So, we've talked about the PMDD storm and how food can be your trusty compass. Now, let's dive deeper into the science behind this delicious alliance. Imagine your body as a finely tuned machine, and your hormones as the conductors of its various functions. During the premenstrual phase, these conductors can get into a bit of a tizzy, throwing everything off balance. This hormonal imbalance is what triggers the storm of PMDD symptoms.

Here's where food comes in: just like choosing the right oil keeps your machine running smoothly, the right foods can help balance those hormonal conductors and calm the PMDD storm. It's all about giving your body the nutrients it craves to feel its best!

The Food-Mood Connection

Ever notice how a sugary treat can send your emotions on a rollercoaster, followed by a crash? That's your blood sugar taking a wild ride! Choosing foods that keep your blood sugar stable can smooth out those emotional swings and keep your mood on an even keel.

Similarly, certain vitamins and minerals act like magic bullets for specific PMDD symptoms. Calcium, for example, can ease those pesky cramps, while magnesium works wonders for anxiety and fatigue. It's about finding the right fuel for your body's individual needs.

Your PMDD Food Toolbox

Here are some key nutritional guidelines to keep in mind:

1. **Befriend fiber:** High-fiber foods like fruits, vegetables, and whole grains keep you feeling full

and content, reducing sugar cravings and preventing those hangry outbursts.

2. **Choose healthy fats:** Omega-3 fatty acids, found in oily fish, flaxseeds, and walnuts, are like tiny mood-boosting cheerleaders, helping to reduce inflammation and keep your brain happy.

3. **Go easy on salt:** Salty foods can exacerbate bloating and water retention, so choose fresh, unprocessed foods and skip the hidden sodium in packaged snacks.

4. **Limit sugar and caffeine:** These can amplify mood swings and anxiety, so opt for naturally sweet fruits and unsweetened herbal teas instead.

5. **Hydrate, hydrate, hydrate:** Water is essential for flushing out toxins and keeping your body functioning smoothly. Aim for eight glasses a day, and more if you're experiencing bloating.

Remember, these are just general guidelines. As you explore the recipes in this book, you'll discover how to customize your diet to match your specific needs and cravings. This is your personal PMDD food adventure, and you get to choose the delicious ingredients that make you feel your best!

CHAPTER 2

Kitchen Staples for PMDD-Friendly Meals: Your Delicious Allies in the Storm

Picture your pantry as a treasure chest overflowing with powerful tools to combat the PMDD storm. Inside, each ingredient is a warrior, ready to fight fatigue, soothe cramps, and keep your mood dancing instead of crashing. But just like any battle, you need the right arsenal. So, let's embark on a grocery shopping adventure and fill your kitchen with PMDD-fighting champions!

Essential Allies for Balanced Battles

1. **Fiber Fortress:** Stock up on fiber-rich friends like whole grains (brown rice, quinoa, oats), legumes (beans, lentils), and vegetables (broccoli, leafy greens, sweet potatoes). They'll keep you feeling full and content, preventing sugar cravings and emotional dips.

2. **Vitamin Vanguard:** These vibrant warriors, like fruits (berries, citrus, avocado) and colorful vegetables (bell peppers, tomatoes, carrots), bring a vitamin and mineral party to your plate. They'll boost your energy, fight inflammation, and keep your brain happy.

3. **Healthy Fat Brigade:** Don't fear fat! Omega-3 fatty acids in fatty fish (salmon, sardines), nuts (walnuts, chia seeds), and olive oil are your mood-boosting allies. They'll reduce inflammation, sharpen your focus, and keep your heart healthy.

4. **Hydration Heroes:** Water is your MVP! Aim for eight glasses a day to flush toxins, promote digestion, and keep your body singing like a well-oiled machine.

Foods to Leave Behind

Not all ingredients are friendly knights! Some, like sugary treats and processed foods, act as sneaky saboteurs, worsening your symptoms and sending your mood on a rollercoaster. So, politely say "no thank you" to:

1. **Sugar Sirens:** Sugary desserts and drinks offer a fleeting high, followed by a crashing low. Stick to naturally sweet fruits and opt for herbal teas instead.

2. **Salty Spies:** Processed foods and excessive salt intake can lead to bloating and water retention. Choose fresh, unprocessed foods and cook from scratch to control your sodium intake.

3. **Caffeine Cannons:** While a morning cup of coffee might seem like a friend, too much caffeine can exacerbate anxiety and disrupt sleep. Limit your intake and explore herbal alternatives like chamomile or peppermint tea.

4. **Alcohol Agents:** Alcohol can disrupt your sleep, worsen mood swings, and interfere with medication. Enjoy it in moderation or opt for non-alcoholic alternatives like mocktails.

CHAPTER 3

General Morning Tips for Energizing Recipes to Conquer the PMDD Storm

Mornings during PMDD can feel like trudging through quicksand. Fatigue whispers in your ear, motivation hides under the pillow, and the mere thought of breakfast seems like a Herculean task. But fear not, weary warrior! This chapter is your breakfast battle cry, filled with energizing recipes, meal prep tips, and gentle nudges to get you out of bed with a spring in your step and sunshine in your soul.

Meal Prep Magic for Busy Mornings

Let's face it, who has time for intricate chopping and whisking when PMDD fatigue hits? Here are some "prep ahead" tricks to make mornings a breeze:

1. **Overnight Oats Extravaganza:** Cook a big batch of oats on the weekend and portion them into jars. Add yogurt, berries, nut butter, or chia

seeds for an endless variety of breakfasts throughout the week.

2. **Hard-Boiled Eggs to the Rescue:** Boil a dozen eggs on Sunday and store them in the fridge. Grab one on the go, slice them over avocado toast, or add them to a quick salad for instant protein power.

3. **Fruit & Veggie Blitz:** Wash and chop your favorite fruits and vegetables in advance. This will make smoothies, yogurt parfaits, and omelets a snap after waking up.

4. **Batch-Bake Muffins & Pancakes:** Whip up a batch of whole-wheat muffins or gluten-free pancakes on a weekend morning. Freeze them individually, and you'll have a healthy, grab-and-go breakfast ready whenever you need it.

Dietary Restrictions? No Problem!

Remember, your PMDD-friendly breakfast shouldn't be limited by food sensitivities. Check out these delicious substitutions:

1. **Gluten-Free Goodness:** Swap rolled oats for quinoa or buckwheat in your overnight oats. Use

gluten-free flour blends for pancakes or try millet bread instead of toast.

2. **Dairy-Free Delight:** Opt for unsweetened almond milk or coconut milk in your smoothie bowl. Top your berries with vegan yogurt or cashew butter for a creamy treat.

3. **Vegan Victory:** Scramble silken tofu with turmeric and nutritional yeast for a savory, plant-based protein boost. Use flaxseed meal as an egg substitute in pancakes, and top your breakfast with tahini or mashed avocado for healthy fats.

Fueling Your Body with the Right Ingredients

Choosing the right ingredients can be like sending tiny superheroes into your body to combat PMDD symptoms. Here are some superstars:

1. **Mood-Boosting Berries:** Blueberries, strawberries, and raspberries are packed with antioxidants and vitamin C, which can reduce anxiety and lift your spirits. Blend them into a

smoothie, toss them over yogurt, or enjoy them fresh for a morning dose of sunshine.

2. **Bloating-Battling Spinach:** This leafy green is rich in magnesium, which helps balance hormones and ease cramping. Add a handful to your smoothie, omelet, or even blend it into your pancake batter for a sneaky nutrient boost.

3. **Fatigue-Fighting Eggs:** A protein powerhouse, eggs provide iron and B vitamins, essential for combating fatigue and keeping your energy levels stable. Scramble them with vegetables, enjoy them boiled for a quick snack, or incorporate them into a baked frittata for a satisfying weekend breakfast.

4. **Brain-Loving Omega-3s:** Fatty fish like salmon or sardines are loaded with omega-3 fatty acids, known for their mood-boosting and brain-supporting properties. Flake some over avocado toast, whip up a quick salmon salad, or try a vegetarian option like walnuts or chia seeds for their plant-based omega-3 goodness.

My Sunrise Ritual: A Personal Touch

Confession time! I'm a sucker for a warm cup of ginger tea with a squeeze of lemon first thing in the morning. It wakes me up gently, soothes my nausea (a frequent PMDD visitor!), and prepares my body for the day ahead. What about you? Share your personal breakfast rituals.

CHAPTER 4

PMDD-Friendly Breakfast Recipes

1. Sunshine Smoothie Bowl (Vegan & Gluten-Free)

Prep Time: 5 minutes

Servings: 1

Ingredients:

- 1 cup unsweetened almond milk
- 1/2 frozen banana
- 1/2 cup frozen berries (mixed or your favorite)
- 1/4 cup spinach

- 1 scoop vegan protein powder (optional)
- 1 tablespoon chia seeds
- 1/4 teaspoon turmeric

Instructions:

I. Blend all ingredients in a blender until smooth and creamy.

II. Pour into a bowl and top with your favorite toppings like fresh berries, chopped nuts, granola, or a drizzle of nut butter.

Nutritional Breakdown:

- Calories: 300 (without protein powder)
- Protein: 10g (with protein powder)
- Fat: 15g
- Carbs: 35g
- Vitamin C: 30% Daily Value
- Manganese: 20% Daily Value

Quick Hack: Make a big batch of the smoothie base and keep it in the fridge for grab-and-go breakfasts throughout the week. Add fresh toppings each morning for variety.

2. Power Pancakes (Gluten-Free & Dairy-Free)

Prep Time: 10 minutes

Cook Time: 10 minutes

Servings: 4

Ingredients:

- 1 cup gluten-free oat flour
- 1/2 cup almond flour
- 1 teaspoon baking powder
- 1/4 teaspoon salt

- 1 cup unsweetened almond milk
- 1 egg (or 1 tablespoon flaxseed meal mixed with 3 tablespoons water)
- 1 tablespoon honey or maple syrup (optional)
- 1/4 teaspoon vanilla extract

Instructions:

I. Whisk dry ingredients in a bowl.

II. In a separate bowl, whisk together almond milk, egg (or flaxseed mixture), honey (if using), and vanilla extract.

III. Pour the wet ingredients into the dry ingredients and stir until just combined. Do not overmix.

IV. Heat a lightly oiled skillet over medium heat. Pour batter into 1/4 cup portions and cook for 2-3 minutes per side, or until golden brown.

V. Serve warm with your favorite toppings like fresh fruit, nut butter, or yogurt.

Nutritional Breakdown:

- Calories: 200 per pancake (without toppings)
- Protein: 5g
- Fat: 8g
- Carbs: 25g
- Fiber: 3g

- Calcium: 10% Daily Value
- Iron: 5% Daily Value

Quick Hack: Make a double batch of batter and freeze individual pancakes for quick breakfasts or snacks. Thaw in the microwave or stovetop before serving.

3. Sunrise Scramble with Spinach and Avocado (Vegetarian)

Prep Time: 5 minutes
Cook Time: 5 minutes

Servings: 1

Ingredients:
- 2 eggs
- 1/2 cup baby spinach
- 1/4 avocado, sliced
- 1/4 teaspoon paprika
- Salt and pepper to taste

Instructions:
I. Whisk eggs with paprika, salt, and pepper in a bowl.
II. Heat a lightly oiled skillet over medium heat. Pour in the egg mixture and cook, stirring occasionally, until scrambled to your desired consistency.
III. Stir in spinach and cook for about 1 minute, or until wilted.
IV. Top with avocado slices and serve with whole-wheat toast or a small side salad.

Nutritional Breakdown:
- Calories: 300
- Protein: 12g
- Fat: 20g (mostly healthy fats from avocado)

- Carbs: 5g
- Vitamin E: 30% Daily Value
- Lutein: 20% Daily Value

Quick Hack: Pre-chop the spinach and avocado the night before for even faster assembly in the morning.

4. Tropical Bliss Oatmeal Bowl (Vegan & Gluten-Free)

Prep Time: 5 minutes

Servings: 1

Ingredients:

- 1/2 cup gluten-free rolled oats

- 1 cup unsweetened coconut milk

- 1/2 cup chopped mango

- 1/4 cup pineapple chunks

- 1/4 cup sliced banana

- 1 tablespoon shredded coconut

- 1/4 teaspoon ground ginger

- Pinch of cinnamon

Instructions:

I. Bring coconut milk to a simmer in a saucepan. Stir in oats, ginger, and cinnamon.

II. Reduce heat and cook for 5 minutes, stirring occasionally, until thickened.

III. Divide oatmeal among two bowls. Top with mango, pineapple, banana, and shredded coconut. Drizzle with additional coconut milk or honey, if desired.

Nutritional Breakdown:

- Calories: 350

- Protein: 5g

- Fat: 15g (mostly healthy fats from coconut)

- Carbs: 50g

- Fiber: 6g

- Vitamin C: 40% Daily Value

- Manganese: 25% Daily Value

Quick Hack: Prep chopped fruit ahead of time for instant bowl assembly. You can also swap the mango and pineapple for other vibrant berries like blueberries or raspberries.

5. Energy Burst Chia Pudding (Vegan & Gluten-Free)

Prep Time: 5 minutes (plus overnight chilling)

Servings: 2

Ingredients:

- 1/2 cup chia seeds

- 1 cup unsweetened almond milk

- 1/4 cup unsweetened shredded coconut

- 1/4 cup chopped dates

- 1/4 teaspoon vanilla extract

- Pinch of sea salt

Instructions:

I. Combine chia seeds, almond milk, coconut, dates, vanilla extract, and salt in a jar or two airtight containers. Stir well and refrigerate overnight.

II. In the morning, stir again and top with additional fruit, nuts, or granola for extra texture and nutrition.

Nutritional Breakdown:

- Calories: 250 per serving

- Protein: 5g

- Fat: 10g (mostly healthy fats from coconut and dates)

- Carbs: 30g

- Fiber: 10g

- Iron: 10% Daily Value

- Calcium: 6% Daily Value

Quick Hack: Make a big batch of the pudding base and keep it in the fridge for quick breakfasts all week. Use different combinations of toppings to keep things interesting.

6. Savory Scrambled Eggs with Smoked Salmon and Artichokes (Vegetarian option available)

Prep Time: 5 minutes
Cook Time: 5 minutes
Servings: 1

Ingredients:

- 2 eggs

- 1/4 cup chopped smoked salmon

- 1/4 cup marinated artichoke hearts, drained and chopped

- 1/4 teaspoon dried dill

- Salt and pepper to taste

- 1 tablespoon olive oil

Instructions:

I. Whisk eggs with dill, salt, and pepper in a bowl.

II. Heat olive oil in a lightly oiled skillet over medium heat. Pour in the egg mixture and cook, stirring occasionally, until scrambled to your desired consistency.

III. Fold in smoked salmon and artichoke hearts. Cook for another minute, until warmed through.

IV. Serve on whole-wheat toast or with a side of avocado slices for added creamy texture.

Vegetarian Option: Replace smoked salmon with 1/4 cup crumbled tempeh or tofu for a plant-based protein boost.

Nutritional Breakdown (with smoked salmon):

- Calories: 350

- Protein: 20g

- Fat: 25g (mostly healthy fats from salmon and olive oil)

- Carbs: 5g

- Vitamin D: 20% Daily Value

- Selenium: 30% Daily Value

Quick Hack: Pre-chop the artichoke hearts the night before for even faster assembly in the morning. You can also use leftover roasted vegetables like peppers or zucchini in this recipe.

7. Berry-licious Overnight Oats (Vegan & Gluten-Free)

Prep Time: 5 minutes (plus overnight chilling)

Servings: 2

Ingredients:

- 1/2 cup rolled oats (gluten-free if needed)

- 1 cup unsweetened almond milk

- 1/4 cup mixed berries (fresh or frozen)

- 1 tablespoon chia seeds

- 1/4 teaspoon vanilla extract

- Pinch of cinnamon

Optional toppings: Chopped nuts, granola, coconut flakes, honey

Instructions:

I. Combine all ingredients in two jars or airtight containers. Stir well and refrigerate overnight.

II. In the morning, give it a good stir and top with your favorite berries, nuts, or granola for extra texture and deliciousness.

Nutritional Breakdown:

- Calories: 250 per serving

- Protein: 5g

- Fat: 10g (mostly healthy fats from chia seeds)

- Carbs: 30g

- Fiber: 8g

- Vitamin C: 20% Daily Value

- Manganese: 15% Daily Value

Quick Hack: Prep a big batch of the base mixture and keep it in the fridge for grab-and-go breakfasts all week. Just mix and match toppings for variety.

8. Sunshine Scramble with Turmeric & Roasted Veggies (Vegan & Gluten-Free)

Prep Time: 10 minutes (plus roasting time for veggies)

Cook Time: 5 minutes

Servings: 1

Ingredients:

- 1/2 cup chopped bell pepper and zucchini (pre-roasted)

- 1/4 cup chopped spinach

- 1/4 cup crumbled tofu

- 1/4 teaspoon turmeric

- Pinch of black pepper

- 1 tablespoon vegetable broth

- 1 tablespoon nutritional yeast (optional)

- Splash of lemon juice

Instructions:

I. Heat a lightly oiled skillet over medium heat. Add bell pepper, zucchini, and spinach. Sauté for 2-3 minutes, until wilted.

II. Crumble in tofu and stir in turmeric, black pepper, and vegetable broth. Cook for another minute, until warmed through.

III. Serve with a sprinkle of nutritional yeast (for cheesy flavor) and a squeeze of lemon juice. Enjoy with whole-wheat toast or a side of avocado.

Nutritional Breakdown:

- Calories: 250

- Protein: 15g

- Fat: 5g

- Carbs: 25g

- Fiber: 5g

- Vitamin C: 20% Daily Value

- Manganese: 10% Daily Value

Quick Hack: Roast a batch of vegetables on the weekend and store them in the fridge for easy scrambling throughout the week. You can also swap the tofu for cooked lentils or beans for a different protein boost.

9. Tropical Smoothie Bowl with Spinach & Spirulina (Vegan & Gluten-Free)

Prep Time: 5 minutes

Servings: 1

Ingredients:

- 1 cup unsweetened coconut milk

- 1/2 frozen banana

- 1/4 cup chopped mango

- 1/4 cup pineapple chunks

- 1/4 cup baby spinach

- 1/2 teaspoon spirulina powder

- Dash of lime juice

Optional toppings: Fresh berries, granola, coconut flakes

Instructions:

I. Blend all ingredients until smooth and creamy.

II. Pour into a bowl and top with your favorite tropical fruits, granola, or coconut flakes for added texture and sweetness.

Nutritional Breakdown:

- Calories: 300

- Protein: 5g

- Fat: 15g (mostly healthy fats from coconut)

- Carbs: 35g

- Fiber: 5g

- Vitamin C: 30% Daily Value

- Manganese: 20% Daily Value

- Iron: 10% Daily Value

Quick Hack: Freeze chopped mango and pineapple in advance for even faster smoothie assembly. You can also add a handful of leafy greens like kale or swiss chard for extra nutrients.

10. Spiced Yogurt Parfait with Chia Seeds & Nuts (Vegetarian & Gluten-Free)

Prep Time: 5 minutes

Servings: 1

Ingredients:

- 1/2 cup plain Greek yogurt

- 1/4 cup chia seeds

- 1/4 cup chopped nuts (walnuts, almonds, or pecans

- 1/4 cup chopped apple or pear (optional)

- 1/4 teaspoon ground cinnamon

- Pinch of nutmeg

- Honey or maple syrup to taste

Instructions:

I. In a small bowl, combine chia seeds, cinnamon, nutmeg, and a splash of honey. Let sit for 5 minutes to plump up.

II. Layer yogurt, chia seed mixture, chopped nuts, and apple or pear slices in a parfait glass. Drizzle with additional honey if desired.

Nutritional Breakdown:

- Calories: 300

- Protein: 15g

- Fat: 15g (mostly healthy fats from nuts)

- Carbs: 25g

- Fiber: 5g

- Calcium: 30% Daily Value

- Vitamin E: 10% Daily Value

Quick Hack: Prepare the chia seed mixture and chop the fruit the night before for even faster assembly in the morning. You can also swap the plain yogurt for flavored varieties like mango or blueberry for a taste twist.

These are just a few ideas to inspire your PMDD-friendly breakfast routine. Remember, listen to your body, choose ingredients that work for you, and most importantly, savor the deliciousness that fuels your mind and body!

CHAPTER 5

PMDD-Friendly Snacks

Let's dive into some delicious and PMDD-friendly snacks to keep your energy stable and your mood soaring throughout the day. Remember, these are just suggestions, feel free to personalize them according to your preferences and dietary needs.

1. **Sunshine Trail Mix**

Prep Time: 5 minutes

Servings: 1

Ingredients:

- 1/4 cup raw almonds or cashews

- 1/4 cup dried cranberries or cherries

- 1/4 cup sunflower seeds or pumpkin seeds

- 1 tablespoon dark chocolate chips (optional)

- Pinch of cinnamon (optional)

Instructions:

I. Combine all ingredients in a small bowl or resealable bag.

II. Enjoy a handful as a mid-morning or afternoon pick-me-up.

Nutritional Breakdown:

- Calories: 200

- Protein: 5g

- Fat: 15g (mostly healthy fats from nuts and seeds)

- Carbs: 15g

- Fiber: 3g

- Manganese: 20% Daily Value

- Iron: 10% Daily Value

Quick Hack: Pre-measure your ingredients in individual bags for grab-and-go convenience. You can also swap in different nuts, seeds, dried fruits, or dark chocolate to mix things up.

2. Creamy Avocado & Tomato Toast

Prep Time: 5 minutes

Servings: 1

Ingredients:

- 1 slice whole-wheat toast

- 1/4 ripe avocado, mashed

- 1/4 cup chopped tomato

- Pinch of sea salt and black pepper

- Fresh basil leaves (optional)

Instructions:

I. Toast the bread and spread with mashed avocado.

II. Top with chopped tomato, salt, pepper, and fresh basil leaves if desired.

- **Nutritional Breakdown:**

- Calories: 200

- Protein: 4g

- Fat: 12g (mostly healthy fats from avocado)

- Carbs: 20g

- Fiber: 4g

- Vitamin C: 20% Daily Value

- Potassium: 10% Daily Value

Quick Hack: Make a bigger batch of mashed avocado in advance and store it in the fridge for easy toast toppings throughout the week. You can also add crumbled feta cheese or a drizzle of balsamic vinegar for extra flavor.

3. Energy-Boosting Smoothie

Prep Time: 5 minutes

Servings: 1

Ingredients:

- 1 cup unsweetened almond milk

- 1/2 frozen banana

- 1/4 cup spinach

- 1/4 cup mixed berries

- 1 scoop vanilla protein powder (optional)

- 1/4 teaspoon ground ginger

Instructions:

I.   Blend all ingredients until smooth and creamy.

II. Enjoy this refreshing and energizing smoothie on the go or as an afternoon pick-me-up.

Nutritional Breakdown:

- Calories: 250 (without protein powder)

- Protein: 10g (with protein powder)

- Fat: 5g

- Carbs: 30g

- Fiber: 5g

- Vitamin C: 30% Daily Value

- Manganese: 20% Daily Value

Quick Hack: Freeze chopped fruit and spinach in advance for even faster smoothie assembly. You can also add other leafy greens like kale or swiss chard for extra nutrients.

4. Sweet & Savory Carrot & Hummus Sticks

Prep Time: 5 minutes

Servings: 1-2

Ingredients:

- 2-3 baby carrots
- 1/4 cup hummus
- Fresh herbs (optional)

Instructions:

I. Wash and cut carrots into sticks.

II. Serve with hummus for a dip and sprinkle with fresh herbs for extra flavor.

Nutritional Breakdown:

- Calories: 150
- Protein: 3g
- Fat: 4g (mostly healthy fats from hummus)
- Carbs: 20g
- Fiber: 3g

- Vitamin A: 300% Daily Value

Quick Hack: Pre-cut the carrots and store them in a container with water for an instant grab-and-go snack. You can also try different types of hummus like roasted red pepper or garlic for a variety of flavors.

5. Blissful Dark Chocolate & Nuts

Prep Time: 2 minutes

Servings: 1

Ingredients:

- 1-2 squares dark chocolate (70% cacao or higher)
- 1/4 cup mixed nuts or seeds

Instructions:

I. Enjoy a few squares of dark chocolate along with a handful of nuts or seeds for a satisfying and mood-boosting treat.

Nutritional Breakdown:

- Calories: 200
- Protein: 5g
- Fat: 12g (mostly healthy fats from nuts and dark chocolate)
- Carbs: 10g
- Fiber: 2g
- Magnesium: 20% Daily Value

- Iron: 10% Daily Value

Quick Hack: Keep a small bag of dark chocolate squares and your favorite nuts in your purse or desk drawer for a readily available mood booster throughout the day

6. Tropical Bliss Yogurt Bowl

Prep Time: 5 minutes

Servings: 1

Ingredients:

- 1/2 cup plain Greek yogurt

- 1/4 cup chopped mango

- 1/4 cup chopped pineapple

- 1/4 cup granola

- 1 tablespoon shredded coconut

- Pinch of cinnamon (optional)

Instructions:

I.   Layer yogurt, mango, pineapple, granola, and coconut in a bowl.

II. Sprinkle with cinnamon if desired and enjoy this refreshing and creamy snack.

Nutritional Breakdown:

- Calories: 300

- Protein: 15g

- Fat: 15g (mostly healthy fats from yogurt and granola)

- Carbs: 25g

- Fiber: 4g

- Vitamin C: 30% Daily Value

- Calcium: 20% Daily Value

Quick Hack: Pre-chop the fruit and store it in a container for easy assembly. You can also swap the yogurt for plant-based alternatives like coconut yogurt or kefir.

7.Spicy Edamame Pods

Prep Time: 5 minutes

Servings: 1

Ingredients:

- 1/2 cup frozen edamame pods, thawed

- 1/2 teaspoon olive oil

- 1/4 teaspoon chili powder

- Pinch of paprika

- Pinch of sea salt

Instructions:

I. Toss edamame pods with olive oil, chili powder, paprika, and salt.

II. Spread on a baking sheet and bake at 400°F for 10-12 minutes, or until lightly browned and crispy.

III. Enjoy these protein-packed pods as a satisfying and flavorful snack.

Nutritional Breakdown:

- Calories: 150

- Protein: 10g

- Fat: 5g (mostly healthy fats from edamame)

- Carbs: 10g

- Fiber: 3g

- Iron: 20% Daily Value

Quick Hack: Double the recipe and store the cooled edamame in an airtight container for a quick grab-and-go snack throughout the week. You can also experiment with different spices like cumin, garlic powder, or cayenne pepper for a variety of flavors.

8.Homemade Trail Mix Bars

Prep Time: 10 minutes

Servings: 4-5 bars

Ingredients:

- 1/2 cup rolled oats

- 1/4 cup chopped nuts (almonds, pecans, walnuts)

- 1/4 cup dried cranberries

- 1/4 cup sunflower seeds

- 1/4 cup pitted dates, chopped

- 1 tablespoon honey or maple syrup

Instructions:

I. Preheat oven to 350°F. Line a baking sheet with parchment paper.

II. Combine all ingredients in a bowl and mix well.

III. Press the mixture evenly onto the baking sheet.

IV. Bake for 15-20 minutes, or until golden brown.

V. Let cool and cut into bars before enjoying.

Nutritional Breakdown:

- Calories: 200 per bar

- Protein: 5g

- Fat: 10g (mostly healthy fats from nuts and seeds)

- Carbs: 25g

- Fiber: 5g

- Manganese: 20% Daily Value

- Iron: 10% Daily Value

Quick Hack: Make a big batch of these bars and store them in the fridge for a convenient snack on the go. You can also customize the recipe with your favorite dried fruits, nuts, and seeds.

9.Roasted Chickpea Crunch

Prep Time: 5 minutes

Cook Time: 20 minutes

Servings: 1

Ingredients:

- 1/2 cup canned chickpeas, drained and rinsed

- 1 tablespoon olive oil

- 1/2 teaspoon curry powder

- 1/4 teaspoon turmeric

- Pinch of sea salt

Instructions:

I. Preheat oven to 400°F. Line a baking sheet with parchment paper.

II. Toss chickpeas with olive oil, curry powder, turmeric, and salt.

III. Spread on the baking sheet and roast for 20-25 minutes, or until crispy and golden brown.

IV. Enjoy these flavorful chickpeas as a crunchy and satisfying snack.

Nutritional Breakdown:

- Calories: 150

- Protein: 5g

- Fat: 5g (mostly healthy fats from olive oil)

- Carbs: 20g

- Fiber: 4g

- Manganese: 20% Daily Value

- Iron: 10% Daily Value

Quick Hack: Pre-make a batch of roasted chickpeas and store them in an airtight container for a quick protein and fiber boost anytime. You can also try different spice combinations like paprika, cumin, or garlic powder for additional flavor variations.

10. Apple & Almond Butter Boats

Prep Time: 5 minutes

Servings: 2

Ingredients:

- 1 apple, cored and sliced

- 2 tablespoons almond butter

- 1/4 teaspoon cinnamon (optional)

Instructions:

I. Fill each apple slice with a dollop of almond butter.

II. Sprinkle with cinnamon if desired and enjoy this healthy and satisfying snack.

Nutritional Breakdown:

- Calories: 150 per apple slice

- Protein: 3g

- Fat: 8g (mostly healthy fats from almond butter)

- Carbs: 20g

- Fiber: 3g

- Vitamin C: 10% Daily Value

- Vitamin E: 5% Daily Value

Quick Hack: Pre-slice the apple and portion out the almond butter in advance for even faster assembly. You can also swap the almond butter for other nut butters like peanut butter or cashew butter.

CHAPTER 6

PMDD-Friendly Lunch Recipes

1. Mediterranean Quinoa Salad

Prep Time: 15 minutes

Serving: 1

Ingredients:

62

- 1/2 cup cooked quinoa

- 1/4 cup chopped cucumber

- 1/4 cup chopped cherry tomatoes

- 1/4 cup crumbled feta cheese

- 1/4 cup kalamata olives, sliced

- 1 tablespoon olive oil

- 1 teaspoon lemon juice

- 1/4 teaspoon dried oregano

- Pinch of salt and pepper

Instructions:

I. Combine cooked quinoa, cucumber, tomatoes, feta, olives, olive oil, lemon juice, oregano, salt, and pepper in a bowl.

II. Toss well and enjoy this refreshing and protein-packed salad for lunch.

Nutritional Breakdown:

- Calories: 350

- Protein: 15g

- Fat: 15g (mostly healthy fats from olive oil and feta)

- Carbs: 35g

- Fiber: 5g

- Vitamin C: 20% Daily Value

- Iron: 10% Daily Value

- Magnesium: 10% Daily Value

Quick Hack: Cook a big batch of quinoa on the weekend for easy lunch assembly throughout the week. Pre-chop the vegetables and store them in airtight containers for extra convenience.

2. Creamy Lentil Soup with Spinach

Prep Time: 10 minutes

Cook Time: 30 minutes

Servings: 2

Ingredients:

- 1/2 cup brown lentils, rinsed

- 1 cup vegetable broth

- 1 cup chopped spinach

- 1/2 cup chopped carrots

- 1/4 cup chopped onion

- 1 clove garlic, minced

- 1 tablespoon olive oil

- 1 teaspoon dried thyme

- Pinch of salt and pepper

Instructions:

I. Heat olive oil in a pot over medium heat. Add onion and garlic, cook until softened.

II. Add carrots and lentils, cook for 5 minutes.

III. Pour in vegetable broth and thyme, bring to a boil, then reduce heat and simmer for 20 minutes or until lentils are tender.

IV. Stir in spinach and cook until wilted. Season with salt and pepper.

V. Enjoy this warming and protein-rich soup for a satisfying lunch.

Nutritional Breakdown:

- Calories: 250 per serving

- Protein: 10g

- Fat: 5g (mostly healthy fats from olive oil)

- Carbs: 35g

- Fiber: 8g

- Iron: 20% Daily Value

- Magnesium: 20% Daily Value

Quick Hack: Make a double batch of this soup and store leftovers in the fridge for lunch throughout the week. You can also use canned lentils for even faster preparation.

3. Salmon & Avocado Sushi Bowls

Prep Time: 15 minutes

Servings: 1

Ingredients:

- 3 ounces cooked salmon, flaked

- 1/2 cup cooked brown rice

- 1/4 avocado, sliced

- 1/4 cup cucumber, sliced

- 1 tablespoon seaweed salad (optional)

- 1 tablespoon sesame seeds

- 1 tablespoon soy sauce or tamari

- 1 teaspoon rice vinegar

Instructions:

I. Divide cooked brown rice evenly into two bowls.

II. Top each bowl with flaked salmon, avocado slices, cucumber slices, seaweed salad (if using), sesame seeds, and a drizzle of soy sauce or tamari.

III. Drizzle with rice vinegar and enjoy this flavorful and protein-packed lunch.

Nutritional Breakdown:

- Calories: 400

- Protein: 30g

- Fat: 20g (mostly healthy fats from salmon and avocado)

- Carbs: 40g

- Fiber: 5g

- Vitamin B12: 100% Daily Value

- Omega-3 fatty acids: 1,000mg

Quick Hack: Cook salmon and brown rice in advance for quick and easy bowl assembly. Pre-chop the vegetables and store them in containers for added convenience.

4. Spicy Black Bean & Sweet Potato Wraps

Prep Time: 15 minutes

Servings: 2

Ingredients:

- 1 large sweet potato, roasted and mashed

- 1/2 cup canned black beans, rinsed and drained

- 1/4 cup chopped red onion

71

- 1/4 cup chopped bell pepper

- 1 tablespoon taco seasoning

- 1 tablespoon salsa

- 1 tablespoon chopped cilantro

- 2 whole-wheat tortillas

Instructions:

I. Combine mashed sweet potato, black beans, red onion, bell pepper, taco seasoning, salsa, and cilantro in a bowl.

II. Spread the mixture evenly on warmed whole-wheat tortillas.

III. Wrap and enjoy this flavorful and filling lunch that's rich in fiber and complex carbohydrates.

Nutritional Breakdown:

- Calories: 350 per wrap
- Protein: 15g
- Fat: 5g (mostly healthy fats from beans)
- Carbs: 50g

- Fiber: 10g
- Vitamin A: 50% Daily Value
- Manganese: 20% Daily Value

Quick Hack: Roast a batch of sweet potatoes on the weekend and store them in the fridge for easy wrap assembly throughout the week. You can also pre-mix the bean and spice mixture and store it in the fridge for even faster preparation.

5. Sunshine Buddha Bowl

Prep Time: 15 minutes

Servings: 1

Ingredients:

- 1/2 cup cooked quinoa

- 1/4 cup roasted chickpeas

- 1/4 cup chopped roasted vegetables (your choice of broccoli, carrots, or bell peppers)

- 1/4 cup chopped mango

- 1/4 cup chopped avocado

- 1 tablespoon tahini dressing (or balsamic vinaigrette)

- 1 teaspoon chopped fresh herbs (basil or parsley)

- Pinch of salt and pepper

Instructions:

I. Divide cooked quinoa into a bowl.

II. Top with roasted chickpeas, vegetables, mango, avocado, tahini dressing, fresh herbs, and salt and pepper.

III. Mix and enjoy this vibrant and satisfying bowl packed with vitamins, minerals, and healthy fats.

Nutritional Breakdown:

- Calories: 350

- Protein: 10g

- Fat: 15g (mostly healthy fats from avocado and tahini)

- Carbs: 35g

- Fiber: 8g

- Vitamin C: 20% Daily Value

- Manganese: 20% Daily Value

Quick Hack: Roast a variety of vegetables on the weekend and store them in the fridge for easy bowl assembly throughout the week. You can also use

pre-cooked quinoa or chickpeas for even faster
preparation.

6. Energizing Chicken Stir-Fry with Cashews

Prep Time: 15 minutes

Cook Time: 15 minutes

Servings: 1

Ingredients:

- 4 ounces boneless, skinless chicken breast, thinly sliced

- 1/2 cup broccoli florets

- 1/4 cup red bell pepper, sliced

- 1/4 cup green beans, trimmed

- 1 tablespoon olive oil

- 1 tablespoon soy sauce or tamari

- 1 tablespoon Sriracha (optional)

- 1/2 teaspoon ginger powder

- 1/4 cup roasted cashews

- Cooked brown rice (for serving)

Instructions:

I. Heat olive oil in a pan over medium-high heat. Add chicken and cook until browned.

II. Stir in broccoli, bell pepper, and green beans. Saute for 5 minutes, or until vegetables are crisp-tender.

III. In a small bowl, combine soy sauce, Sriracha (if using), and ginger powder. Pour into the pan and stir to coat.

IV. Cook for another minute, then sprinkle with cashews.

V. Serve over cooked brown rice for a flavorful and protein-packed lunch.

Nutritional Breakdown:

- Calories: 400

- Protein: 30g

- Fat: 15g (mostly healthy fats from cashews and olive oil)

- Carbs: 30g

- Fiber: 5g

- Vitamin C: 20% Daily Value

- Iron: 10% Daily Value

Quick Hack: Pre-marinate the chicken in soy sauce and ginger powder for extra flavor and save time during cooking. You can also roast the cashews in advance for added crunch.

7. Cozy lentil & Veggie Shepherd's Pie

Prep Time: 15 minutes

Cook Time: 45 minutes

Servings: 2

Ingredients:

- 1 cup brown lentils, rinsed

- 1 cup chopped sweet potato

- 1 cup chopped carrots

- 1/2 cup chopped onion

- 1 clove garlic, minced

- 1 tablespoon olive oil

- 1 teaspoon dried thyme

- 1/2 cup vegetable broth

- 1/4 cup mashed potatoes

- Salt and pepper to taste

Instructions:

I. Preheat oven to 400°F. Heat olive oil in a pot over medium heat. Add onion and garlic, cook until softened.

II. Stir in carrots, sweet potato, and thyme. Cook for 5 minutes.

III. Add lentils and vegetable broth. Bring to a boil, then reduce heat and simmer for 20 minutes, or until lentils are tender.

IV. Season with salt and pepper to taste. Top with mashed potatoes and bake for 20 minutes, or until golden brown.

V. Enjoy this hearty and comforting lunch that's rich in plant-based protein and fiber.

Nutritional Breakdown:

- Calories: 350 per serving

- Protein: 15g

- Fat: 5g (mostly healthy fats from olive oil)

- Carbs: 50g

- Fiber: 10g

- Vitamin C: 20% Daily Value

- Manganese: 20% Daily Value

Quick Hack: Cook a big batch of lentils and mashed potatoes on the weekend for quick and easy assembly throughout the week. You can also use pre-cooked sweet potatoes for even faster preparation.

8. Zesty Tuna Salad Lettuce Wraps

Prep Time: 15 minutes

Servings: 2

Ingredients:

- 2 cans tuna, drained and flaked

- 1/4 cup chopped cucumber

- 1/4 cup chopped celery

- 1/4 cup chopped red onion

- 1 tablespoon Greek yogurt

- 1 tablespoon lemon juice

- 1/2 teaspoon Dijon mustard

- 1/4 teaspoon dill weed

- Pinch of salt and pepper

- Romaine lettuce leaves (for wrapping)

Instructions:

- In a bowl, combine tuna, cucumber, celery, red onion, Greek yogurt, lemon juice, Dijon mustard, dill weed, salt, and pepper.

- Mix well and spoon the mixture into romaine lettuce leaves for wraps.

- Enjoy this light and refreshing lunch that's packed with protein and healthy fats.

Nutritional Breakdown:

- Calories: 250 per wrap

- Protein: 25g
- Fat: 5g (mostly healthy fats from tuna and yogurt)
- Carbs: 5g
- Vitamin C: 10% Daily Value
- Magnesium: 10% Daily Value
- Selenium: 20% Daily Value

Quick Hack: Pre-chop the vegetables and store them in airtight containers for easy assembly throughout the week. You can also use canned salmon or sardines for a similar protein boost.

9. Smoky Tofu Scramble with Avocado Toast

Prep Time: 15 minutes

Cook Time: 10 minutes

Servings: 1

Ingredients:

- 1/2 block firm tofu, crumbled

- 1/4 cup chopped bell pepper

- 1/4 cup chopped onion

- 1/4 teaspoon smoked paprika

- 1/4 teaspoon turmeric

- 1 tablespoon olive oil

- 1 slice whole-wheat toast

- 1/4 avocado, sliced

- Salt and pepper to taste

Instructions:

I. Heat olive oil in a pan over medium heat. Add bell pepper and onion, cook until softened.

II. Stir in crumbled tofu, paprika, and turmeric. Cook for 5 minutes, or until tofu is golden brown.

III. Season with salt and pepper to taste.

IV. Toast whole-wheat bread and top with sliced avocado and the tofu scramble.

V. Enjoy this protein-packed and flavorful lunch that's packed with plant-based goodness.

Nutritional Breakdown:

- Calories: 350

- Protein: 20g

- Fat: 15g (mostly healthy fats from avocado and olive oil)

- Carbs: 30g

- Fiber: 5g

- Manganese: 20% Daily Value

- Iron: 10% Daily Value

Quick Hack: Pre-crumble the tofu and chop the vegetables in advance for even faster meal assembly. You can also use pre-cooked brown rice as an alternative to toast for a more filling option.

10. Creamy Pumpkin & Chickpea Curry with Rice

Prep Time: 15 minutes

Cook Time: 30 minutes

Servings: 2

Ingredients:

- 1 cup canned pumpkin puree

- 1 can chickpeas, drained and rinsed

- 1 cup vegetable broth

- 1/2 cup chopped onion

- 1 clove garlic, minced

- 1 tablespoon curry powder

- 1 teaspoon garam masala

- 1/2 teaspoon ginger powder

- 1/4 cup coconut milk

- Cooked brown rice (for serving)

Instructions:

I. Heat olive oil in a pot over medium heat. Add onion and garlic, cook until softened.

II. Stir in curry powder, garam masala, and ginger powder. Cook for 1 minute, until fragrant.

III. Add pumpkin puree, chickpeas, and vegetable broth. Bring to a boil, then reduce heat and simmer for 20 minutes.

IV. Stir in coconut milk and heat through.

V. Serve over cooked brown rice for a comforting and flavorful lunch that's rich in plant-based protein and fiber.

Nutritional Breakdown:

- Calories: 300 per serving

- Protein: 15g

- Fat: 5g (mostly healthy fats from coconut milk)

- Carbs: 40g

- Fiber: 8g

- Vitamin A: 50% Daily Value

- Manganese: 20% Daily Value

Quick Hack: Use leftover roasted pumpkin from another recipe to save time and add extra flavor.

CHAPTER 7

PMDD-Soothing Dinner Recipes

Let's turn your dinner time into a PMDD-soothing sanctuary with these 7 delightful and nourishing recipes:

1. Creamy Salmon & Spinach Pasta

Prep Time: 15 minutes

Cook Time: 20 minutes

Servings: 2

Ingredients:

- 4 ounces salmon fillets, cooked and flaked

- 1 cup cooked whole-wheat pasta

- 1/2 cup frozen spinach, thawed

- 1/4 cup ricotta cheese

- 1/4 cup milk (dairy or plant-based)

- 1 tablespoon lemon juice

- 1 teaspoon dried dill

- Pinch of salt and pepper

- Parmesan cheese (optional)

Instructions:

I. Cook pasta according to package directions. While pasta cooks, heat milk in a pan over medium heat. Stir in ricotta cheese, lemon juice, dill, salt, and pepper until a creamy sauce forms.

II. Add cooked and flaked salmon, spinach, and cooked pasta to the sauce. Stir gently to combine and warm through.

III. Serve with a sprinkle of Parmesan cheese (optional) and enjoy this comforting and protein-rich dish.

Nutritional Breakdown:

- Calories: 400 per serving

- Protein: 30g

- Fat: 15g (mostly healthy fats from salmon and ricotta)

- Carbs: 35g

- Fiber: 5g

- Vitamin B12: 100% Daily Value

- Omega-3 fatty acids: 1,000mg

Quick Hack: Leftover roasted salmon or canned salmon can be used in this recipe for even faster preparation. You can also use frozen or pre-washed spinach for added convenience.

2. Cozy Sweet Potato & Lentil Curry

Prep Time: 15 minutes

Cook Time: 30 minutes

Servings: 4

Ingredients:

- 1 tablespoon olive oil

- 1 onion, chopped

- 2 cloves garlic, minced

- 1 tablespoon curry powder

- 1 teaspoon ground turmeric

- 1/2 teaspoon chili powder (optional)

- 1 cup brown lentils, rinsed

- 4 cups vegetable broth

- 1 sweet potato, diced

- 1 can (15 oz) diced tomatoes, undrained

- 1 cup chopped kale or spinach

- 1/2 cup cooked brown rice (for serving)

- Fresh cilantro (optional)

Instructions:

I.   Heat olive oil in a pot over medium heat. Add
     onion and cook until softened. Stir in garlic, curry

powder, turmeric, and chili powder (if using). Saute for 1 minute.

II. Add lentils, vegetable broth, sweet potato, and tomatoes. Bring to a boil, then reduce heat and simmer for 20 minutes, or until lentils and sweet potato are tender.

III. Stir in kale or spinach and cook for 1-2 minutes, or until wilted.

IV. Serve over cooked brown rice and garnish with fresh cilantro (optional).

Nutritional Breakdown:

- Calories: 350 per serving

- Protein: 15g

- Fat: 5g (mostly healthy fats from olive oil)

- Carbs: 50g

- Fiber: 10g

- Vitamin C: 30% Daily Value

- Manganese: 20% Daily Value

Quick Hack: Cook a big batch of brown rice or lentils on the weekend for easy dinner assembly throughout the week. You can also use pre-chopped vegetables or frozen mixed vegetables for added convenience.

3.Salmon & Asparagus Foil Packets

Prep Time: 10 minutes

Cook Time: 20 minutes

Servings: 2

Ingredients:

- 2 salmon fillets

- 1 bunch asparagus, trimmed

- 1/4 cup lemon juice

- 1 tablespoon olive oil

- 1 teaspoon dried tarragon

- Pinch of salt and pepper

- Aluminum foil pouches

Instructions:

I.   Preheat oven to 400°F. Tear off two large pieces of aluminum foil.

II. Place a salmon fillet on each foil pouch. Top with asparagus, drizzle with lemon juice and olive oil, sprinkle with tarragon, salt, and pepper.

III. Fold the pouch closed, making sure it's well-sealed.

IV. Place pouches on a baking sheet and bake for 15-20 minutes, or until salmon is cooked through and asparagus is tender.

V. Open pouches carefully (steam will release) and enjoy this simple and flavorful dish.

Nutritional Breakdown:

- Calories: 400 per serving

- Protein: 30g

- Fat: 15g (mostly healthy fats from salmon and olive oil)

- Carbs: 5g

- Vitamin C: 20% Daily Value

- Vitamin B12: 100% Daily Value

- Omega-3 fatty acids: 1,000mg

Quick Hack: Pre-cut the asparagus and store it in a bag in the fridge for faster assembly. You can also use pre-seasoned lemon pepper for added convenience.

4. Creamy Pumpkin & Chickpea Soup

Prep Time: 15 minutes

Cook Time: 30 minutes

Servings: 4

Ingredients:

- 1 tablespoon olive oil

- 1 onion, chopped

- 2 cloves garlic, minced

- 1 teaspoon ground cumin

- 1/2 teaspoon ground coriander

- Pinch of cayenne pepper (optional)

- 1 can (15 oz) pumpkin puree

- 4 cups vegetable broth

- 1 can (15 oz) chickpeas, drained and rinsed

- 1/2 cup coconut milk (full-fat or light)

- Salt and pepper to taste

- Chopped fresh parsley (optional)

Instructions:

I. Heat olive oil in a pot over medium heat. Add onion and cook until softened. Stir in garlic, cumin, coriander, and cayenne pepper (if using). Saute for 1 minute.

II. Add pumpkin puree, vegetable broth, chickpeas, and coconut milk. Bring to a boil, then reduce heat and simmer for 20 minutes.

III. Use an immersion blender or transfer soup to a blender and puree until smooth. Season with salt and pepper to taste.

IV. Serve hot, garnished with chopped fresh parsley (optional).

Nutritional Breakdown:

- Calories: 300 per serving

- Protein: 10g

- Fat: 10g (mostly healthy fats from coconut milk)

- Carbs: 40g

- Fiber: 5g

- Vitamin A: 50% Daily Value

- Manganese: 20% Daily Value

Quick Hack: Use pre-chopped onion and frozen chopped peppers for added convenience. You can also roast and puree a butternut squash instead of using canned pumpkin puree.

5. One-Pan Chicken & Veggie Roast

Prep Time: 15 minutes

Cook Time: 40 minutes

Servings: 4

Ingredients:

- 1 pound boneless, skinless chicken breasts or thighs

- 1 tablespoon olive oil

- 1/2 teaspoon dried thyme

- Pinch of salt and pepper

- 1 cup chopped Brussels sprouts

- 1 cup chopped sweet potato

- 1/2 cup chopped red onion

- 1/4 cup balsamic vinegar

- 1 tablespoon honey

Instructions:

I. Preheat oven to 400°F. Toss chicken in olive oil, thyme, salt, and pepper.

II. On a baking sheet, arrange chicken, Brussels sprouts, sweet potato, and red onion.

III. In a small bowl, whisk together balsamic vinegar and honey. Drizzle over vegetables and chicken.

IV. Bake for 40 minutes, or until chicken is cooked through and vegetables are tender.

V. Enjoy this easy and flavorful one-pan dinner that's packed with protein and vegetables.

Nutritional Breakdown:

- Calories: 400 per serving

- Protein: 30g

- Fat: 15g (mostly healthy fats from olive oil)

- Carbs: 30g

- Fiber: 5g

- Vitamin C: 20% Daily Value

- Potassium: 20% Daily Value

Quick Hack: Pre-cut the vegetables and store them in an airtight container in the fridge for even faster assembly. You can also use boneless, skinless chicken thighs for extra flavor and moisture.

6. Spicy Black Bean & Quinoa Stuffed Peppers

Prep Time: 15 minutes

Cook Time: 30 minutes

Servings: 2

Ingredients:

- 2 bell peppers, halved and seeded

- 1 tablespoon olive oil

- 1 onion, chopped

- 2 cloves garlic, minced

- 1 cup cooked black beans

- 1/2 cup cooked quinoa

- 1/4 cup chopped corn

- 1/4 cup chopped red bell pepper

- 1 tablespoon taco seasoning

- 1/4 cup salsa

- 1/4 cup shredded cheese (Monterey Jack or cheddar)

- Cilantro and avocado slices (optional)

Instructions:

I.   Preheat oven to 400°F. Heat olive oil in a pan over medium

II. Heat olive oil in a pan over medium heat. Add onion and cook until softened. Stir in garlic, cook for an additional minute.

III. Add cooked black beans, quinoa, corn, red bell pepper, taco seasoning, and salsa. Mix well and cook for 2-3 minutes, warming through and allowing the flavors to meld.

IV. Spoon the mixture into the prepared bell pepper halves. Top with shredded cheese and bake for 15-20 minutes, or until cheese is melted and bubbly.

V. Garnish with cilantro and avocado slices (optional) before serving.

Nutritional Breakdown:

- Calories: 350 per pepper
- Protein: 15g
- Fat: 5g (mostly healthy fats from beans and avocado)
- Carbs: 40g
- Fiber: 10g
- Vitamin C: 30% Daily Value
- Iron: 20% Daily Value

Quick Hack: Cook a big batch of quinoa on the weekend for easy stuffing preparation throughout the week. You can also use canned black beans and frozen corn for added convenience.

7. Creamy Tomato & White Bean Soup with Pesto Swirl

Prep Time: 15 minutes

Cook Time: 30 minutes

Servings: 4

Ingredients:

- 1 tablespoon olive oil

- 1 onion, chopped

- 2 cloves garlic, minced

- 1 can (28 oz) diced tomatoes, undrained

- 4 cups vegetable broth

- 1 can (15 oz) cannellini beans, drained and
  rinsed

- 1/2 cup heavy cream (dairy or plant-based)

- 1/4 cup pesto

- Salt and pepper to taste

- Fresh basil leaves (optional)

Instructions:

I. Heat olive oil in a pot over medium heat. Add
    onion and cook until softened. Stir in garlic, cook
    for an additional minute.

II. Add diced tomatoes, vegetable broth, cannellini beans, and heavy cream. Bring to a boil, then reduce heat and simmer for 20 minutes, allowing the flavors to develop.

III. Use an immersion blender or transfer soup to a blender and puree until smooth. Season with salt and pepper to taste.

IV. Swirl in pesto just before serving, creating a beautiful and flavorful contrast. Garnish with fresh basil leaves (optional).

Nutritional Breakdown:

- Calories: 350 per serving

- Protein: 10g

- Fat: 15g (mostly healthy fats from cream and pesto)

- Carbs: 40g

- Fiber: 5g

- Vitamin C: 20% Daily Value

- Vitamin K: 20% Daily Value

Quick Hack: Use pre-chopped onion and frozen chopped garlic for added convenience. You can also substitute white beans for cannellini beans or even chickpeas for a different flavor profile.

8. Turmeric Chicken & Coconut Curry

Prep Time: 15 minutes

Cook Time: 30 minutes

Servings: 4

Ingredients:

- 1 tablespoon olive oil

- 1 onion, chopped

- 2 cloves garlic, minced

- 1 tablespoon grated ginger

- 1 tablespoon curry powder

- 1 teaspoon turmeric

- 1/2 teaspoon chili powder (optional)

- 1 can (15 oz) coconut milk

- 4 cups vegetable broth

- 1 pound boneless, skinless chicken breasts or thighs, cubed

- 1 cup chopped bell peppers (your choice of colors)

- 1 cup chopped broccoli florets

- 1 cup cooked brown rice (for serving)

- Fresh cilantro leaves (optional)

Instructions:

I. Heat olive oil in a pot over medium heat. Add onion and cook until softened. Stir in garlic and ginger, cook for an additional minute.

II. Add curry powder, turmeric, and chili powder (if using). Saute for 1 minute, allowing the spices to bloom.

III. Pour in coconut milk and vegetable broth. Bring to a boil, then reduce heat and simmer for 5 minutes.

IV. Add chicken, bell peppers, and broccoli. Simmer for 15-20 minutes, or until chicken is cooked through and vegetables are tender.

V. Serve over cooked brown rice and garnish with fresh cilantro leaves (optional).

Nutritional Breakdown:

- Calories: 400 per serving

- Protein: 30g

- Fat: 15g (mostly healthy fats from coconut milk)

- Carbs: 30g

- Fiber: 5g

- Vitamin C: 20% Daily Value

- Manganese: 20% Daily Value

Quick Hack: Use pre-chopped or frozen vegetables for added convenience. You can also substitute chicken with tofu or tempeh for a vegetarian option.

9. Spicy Lentil & Sweet Potato Skillet

Prep Time: 15 minutes

Cook Time: 30 minutes

Servings: 2

Ingredients:

- 1 tablespoon olive oil

- 1 onion, chopped

- 2 cloves garlic, minced

- 1/2 teaspoon ground cumin

- 1/4 teaspoon chili powder

- 1 cup brown lentils, rinsed

- 1 cup diced sweet potato

- 1 can (14.5 oz) diced tomatoes, undrained

- 1/2 cup vegetable broth

- 1/4 cup chopped fresh cilantro

- Lime wedges (optional)

Instructions:

I. Heat olive oil in a large skillet over medium heat. Add onion and cook until softened. Stir in garlic, cumin, and chili powder. Saute for 1 minute.

II. Add lentils, sweet potato, diced tomatoes, and vegetable broth. Bring to a boil, then reduce heat and simmer for 20-25 minutes, or until lentils are tender and sweet potato is cooked through.

III. Stir in fresh cilantro and cook for an additional minute.

IV. Serve hot with lime wedges (optional).

Nutritional Breakdown:

- Calories: 350 per serving

- Protein: 15g

- Fat: 5g (mostly healthy fats from olive oil)

- Carbs: 50g

- Fiber: 10g

- Vitamin C: 30% Daily Value

- Iron: 20% Daily Value

Quick Hack: Cook a big batch of brown lentils on the weekend for easy dinner assembly throughout the week. You can also use pre-chopped vegetables or frozen mixed vegetables for added convenience.

10. Roasted Salmon & Cherry Tomato Farro Salad

Prep Time: 15 minutes

Cook Time: 30 minutes

Servings: 2

Ingredients:

- 1 salmon fillet

- 1 tablespoon olive oil

- 1/2 teaspoon dried thyme

- Pinch of salt and pepper

- 1 cup cherry tomatoes, halved

- 1/2 cup cooked farro

- 1/4 cup crumbled feta cheese

- 1 tablespoon lemon juice

- 1 tablespoon olive oil (for dressing)

- Fresh parsley, chopped (optional)

Instructions:

I. Preheat oven to 400°F. Season salmon fillet with olive oil, thyme, salt, and pepper.

II. Place salmon on a baking sheet and roast for 15-20 minutes, or until cooked through.

III. While salmon cooks, toss cherry tomatoes and cooked farro in a bowl.

IV. In a small bowl, Whisk together lemon juice and olive oil for a simple dressing.

V. Once salmon is cooked, flake it into the salad bowl with the tomatoes and farro. Drizzle with dressing and gently toss to combine.

VI. Crumble feta cheese over the salad and garnish with fresh parsley (optional).

Nutritional Breakdown:

- Calories: 400 per serving

- Protein: 30g

- Fat: 15g (mostly healthy fats from salmon and olive oil)

- Carbs: 35g

- Fiber: 5g

- Vitamin C: 20% Daily Value

- Vitamin B12: 100% Daily Value

- Omega-3 fatty acids: 1,000mg

Quick Hack: Cook a batch of farro on the weekend for easy salad assembly throughout the week. You can also use pre-chopped parsley or other fresh herbs for added flavor and nutrient variety.

Remember, these are just a starting point! Feel free to personalize these recipes to your preferences and dietary needs. Explore different flavors, textures, and ingredients to find what works best for you and keeps you feeling satisfied and supported throughout your evening.

With these diverse and comforting dinner options, you can navigate your PMDD fluctuations with confidence, knowing you have a variety of satisfying and nourishing meals to nurture your body and mind.

CHAPTER 8

PMDD-Friendly Desserts without Compromise

Navigating PMDD often means seeking comforting flavors without compromising your well-being. Let's explore delicious desserts that satisfy your sweet tooth while supporting your nutritional needs:

1. Dark Chocolate & Raspberry Smoothie Bowl

Prep Time: 5 minutes

Servings: 1

Ingredients:

- 1 frozen banana
- 1/2 cup frozen raspberries
- 1/2 cup unsweetened almond milk (or milk of your choice)
- 1 scoop cacao powder or protein powder
- 1 tablespoon natural peanut butter
- 1-2 squares dark chocolate (70% or higher cacao)

Instructions:

I. Blend frozen banana, raspberries, almond milk, cacao powder, and peanut butter until smooth.

II. Pour into a bowl and top with shaved or chopped dark chocolate.

III. Enjoy the creamy and antioxidant-rich treat!

Nutritional Perks:

- Fiber, protein, and healthy fats support satiety and energy levels.
- Dark chocolate offers magnesium and mood-boosting benefits.
- Raspberries provide vitamin C and antioxidants.

2. Baked Apples with Cinnamon & Nuts

Prep Time: 15 minutes

Cook Time: 30 minutes

Servings: 4

Ingredients:

- 4 apples, cored and halved
- 1/4 cup chopped walnuts or pecans
- 1/4 cup rolled oats
- 1/4 teaspoon ground cinnamon
- 1/4 teaspoon nutmeg
- 1 tablespoon honey or maple syrup (optional)

Instructions:

I.   Preheat oven to 375°F.

II. Combine chopped nuts, oats, cinnamon, and nutmeg in a bowl.

III. Stuff each apple half with the oat mixture. Drizzle with honey or maple syrup (optional).

IV. Place apples on a baking sheet and bake for 30 minutes, or until tender and golden brown.

V. Enjoy a warm and comforting dessert packed with fiber and vitamins.

Nutritional Perks:

- Apples are rich in fiber and vitamin C, supporting digestion and immunity.

- Nuts provide healthy fats and protein for sustained energy.

- Cinnamon offers anti-inflammatory benefits and blood sugar regulation.

3. No-Bake Chia Seed Pudding with Mango & Coconut

Prep Time: 10 minutes

Chill Time: 4 hours

Servings: 2

Ingredients:

- 1/2 cup chia seeds
- 1 cup unsweetened almond milk (or milk of your choice)
- 1/4 cup chopped mango
- 1/4 cup shredded unsweetened coconut
- 1 teaspoon honey or maple syrup (optional)
- Pinch of vanilla extract

Instructions:

I. Combine chia seeds, almond milk, honey/maple syrup (optional), and vanilla extract in a jar. Stir well and let sit for 5 minutes.
II. Stir in chopped mango and refrigerate for at least 4 hours, or overnight, until pudding thickens.
III. Top with shredded coconut before serving.
IV. Enjoy a refreshing and nutrient-rich treat ideal for hot flashes or cravings.

Nutritional Perks:

- Chia seeds offer fiber, omega-3 fatty acids, and protein for sustained energy.
- Mango adds vitamin C and antioxidants for a radiant complexion.
- Coconut provides healthy fats and a tropical touch.

4. Baked Sweet Potato Brownies with Dark Chocolate Chips

Prep Time: 15 minutes

Cook Time: 30 minutes

Servings: 12

Ingredients:

- 1 cup mashed roasted sweet potato
- 1/2 cup almond flour
- 1/4 cup unsweetened cocoa powder
- 1/4 cup chopped walnuts or pecans
- 1/4 cup honey or maple syrup
- 1 egg
- 1/2 teaspoon baking powder
- 1/4 cup dark chocolate chips (70% or higher cacao)

Instructions:

I. Preheat oven to 350°F. Line a baking sheet with parchment paper.

II. Combine mashed sweet potato, almond flour, cocoa powder, nuts, honey/maple syrup, egg, and baking powder in a bowl. Mix well.

III. Fold in dark chocolate chips.

IV. Spread batter evenly in the prepared baking sheet.

V. Bake for 30 minutes, or until a toothpick inserted comes out clean.

VI. Enjoy these fudgy and nutritious brownies!

Nutritional Perks:

- Sweet potato offers natural sweetness, fiber, and vitamin A.
- Almond flour and cocoa powder add protein and antioxidants.
- Nuts contribute healthy fats and texture.
- Dark chocolate provides magnesium and mood-boosting benefits.

5. Frozen Yogurt Bark with Berries & Nuts

Prep Time: 10 minutes

Freeze Time: 4 hours

Servings: 6-8

Ingredients:

- 1 cup plain Greek yogurt (full-fat or low-fat)
- 1/4 cup honey or maple syrup
- 1/4 cup chopped nuts (almonds, pistachios, etc.)
- 1/2 cup fresh berries (blueberries, raspberries, etc.)

Instructions:

I. Line a baking sheet with parchment paper.

II. Pour yogurt into a bowl and stir in honey/maple syrup until smooth.

III. Spread the yogurt evenly onto the prepared baking sheet.

IV. Sprinkle with chopped nuts and arrange berries on top.

V. Freeze for at least 4 hours, or until solid.

VI. Break into pieces and enjoy a refreshing and healthy snack!

Nutritional Perks:

- Greek yogurt offers protein and calcium for muscle support and bone health.
- Honey/maple syrup adds a touch of sweetness without relying on refined sugars.
- Nuts provide healthy fats and fiber for satiety.
- Berries are rich in antioxidants and vitamins for cell protection and general well-being.

6. Baked Figs with Honey & Walnuts

Prep Time: 10 minutes

Cook Time: 20 minutes

Servings: 4

Ingredients:

- 4 fresh figs, halved
- 1 tablespoon honey
- 1/4 cup chopped walnuts
- 1/4 teaspoon ground cinnamon
- Pinch of nutmeg

Instructions:

I.   Preheat oven to 375°F. Line a baking sheet with parchment paper.

II. Place fig halves on the baking sheet, cut side up. Drizzle each with honey.

III. Sprinkle walnuts, cinnamon, and nutmeg over the figs.

IV. Bake for 20 minutes, or until figs are slightly softened and golden brown.

V. Enjoy a warm and decadent dessert rich in antioxidants and healthy fats.

Nutritional Perks:

- Figs provide fiber, potassium, and antioxidants for digestion and cell health.
- Honey offers natural sweetness and a touch of magnesium.
- Walnuts contribute healthy fats, protein, and omega-3 fatty acids.
- Cinnamon and nutmeg add warming flavors and potential blood sugar regulation benefits.

7. Dark Chocolate & Coconut Milk Mousse

Prep Time: 10 minutes

Chill Time: 2 hours

Servings: 2

Ingredients:

- 1 can (13.5 oz) full-fat coconut milk, chilled
- 1/2 cup chopped dark chocolate (70% or higher cacao)
- 1/4 teaspoon vanilla extract
- Pinch of sea salt

Instructions:

I. Melt dark chocolate in a double boiler or microwave, stirring frequently.

II. In a chilled bowl, whip coconut milk until stiff peaks form.

III. Gently fold melted chocolate, vanilla extract, and salt into the whipped coconut milk.

IV. Spoon mousse into individual serving dishes and refrigerate for at least 2 hours.

V. Indulge in a luxurious and creamy treat with healthy fats and magnesium.

Nutritional Perks:

- Coconut milk offers healthy fats, protein, and MCTs for sustained energy.
- Dark chocolate provides magnesium, antioxidants, and potential mood-boosting benefits.
- Vanilla extract adds a touch of fragrance and potential calming effects.

8. Roasted Pears with Almond Butter & Cranberries

Prep Time: 10 minutes

Cook Time: 20 minutes

Servings: 2

Ingredients:

- 2 pears, cored and halved
- 2 tablespoons almond butter
- 1/4 cup dried cranberries
- 1/4 teaspoon ground cinnamon
- Pinch of nutmeg

Instructions:

I. Preheat oven to 375°F. Line a baking sheet with parchment paper.

II. Place pear halves on the baking sheet, cut side up.

III. Spread each pear half with almond butter and sprinkle with cranberries, cinnamon, and nutmeg.

IV. Bake for 20 minutes, or until pears are tender and golden brown.

V. Enjoy a comforting and fiber-rich dessert with healthy fats and tart sweetness.

Nutritional Perks:

- Pears are rich in fiber and vitamin C for digestion and immunity.
- Almond butter provides protein, healthy fats, and prebiotics for gut health.
- Cranberries offer antioxidants and a tart counterpoint to sweetness.
- Cinnamon and nutmeg add warming flavors and potential blood sugar regulation benefits.

9. Banana Ice Cream with Berries & Cacao Nibs

Prep Time: 5 minutes

Freeze Time: 2 hours

Servings: 2

Ingredients:

- 2 frozen bananas, chopped
- 1/4 cup frozen berries (your choice)
- 1 tablespoon unsweetened cocoa powder
- 1/4 cup almond milk (optional)
- 1 tablespoon cacao nibs

Instructions:

I. Blend frozen bananas, berries, and cocoa powder until smooth and creamy. Add almond milk if needed for desired consistency.
II. Scoop "ice cream" into bowls and top with cacao nibs.
III. Enjoy a refreshing and nutrient-rich treat packed with potassium, antioxidants, and a natural chocolatey twist.

Nutritional Perks:
- Bananas offer potassium, fiber, and natural sweetness.
- Berries contribute antioxidants and vitamins for vibrant health.
- Cocoa powder adds antioxidants and a touch of rich flavor.
- Cacao nibs provide healthy fats, magnesium, and a satisfying crunch.

10. Chia Seed Pudding with Pumpkin Spice & Pecans

Prep Time: 10 minutes

Chill Time: 4 hours

Servings: 2

Ingredients:

- 1/2 cup chia seeds
- 1 cup unsweetened almond milk (or milk of your choice)
- 1/2 cup pumpkin puree

- 1/4 teaspoon pumpkin pie spice
- 1 tablespoon honey or maple syrup (optional)
- 1/4 cup chopped pecans
- Pinch of sea salt

Instructions:

I. Combine chia seeds, almond milk, pumpkin puree, pumpkin pie spice, and honey/maple syrup (optional) in a jar. Stir well and let sit for 5 minutes.

II. Refrigerate for at least 4 hours, or overnight, until pudding thickens.

III. Top with chopped pecans and a sprinkle of sea salt before serving.

IV. Enjoy a creamy and autumnal dessert rich in fiber, protein, and healthy fats.

Nutritional Perks:

- Chia seeds offer fiber, omega-3 fatty acids, and protein for sustained energy.
- Pumpkin puree adds vitamin A, fiber, and a warm, seasonal flavor.
- Pumpkin pie spice provides antioxidants and warming spices like cinnamon and ginger.

- Pecans contribute healthy fats, protein, and a satisfying crunch.

This concludes our journey through PMDD-friendly desserts that prioritize both indulgence and well-being. Remember, these are just a starting point! Feel free to customize these recipes and explore your own creative avenues to find desserts that nourish your body and satisfy your sweet tooth during PMDD fluctuations.

I hope this collection empowers you to navigate your PMDD with delicious solutions and empowers you to make choices that support your physical and emotional needs.

CHAPTER 9

Beverages for Relaxation: Soothe Your PMDD with Hydrating Elixirs

PMDD often brings a wave of physical and emotional symptoms. Soothing beverages can be your allies, promoting hydration, easing discomfort, and encouraging relaxation. Let's explore nine calming drink options:

1. Cozy Chamomile Tea

- Brew chamomile tea bags or loose-leaf chamomile in hot water for 5-10 minutes.

- Add a squeeze of lemon or honey for extra flavor and potential mood-boosting benefits.
- Chamomile offers anti-inflammatory and calming properties, ideal for easing cramps and anxiety.

2. Mint Mojito Mocktail

- Muddle fresh mint leaves with a wedge of lime in a glass.
- Fill with ice and top with sparkling water or club soda.
- Garnish with fresh mint leaves and a lime wedge.
- This refreshing and hydrating drink provides vitamin C and the calming properties of mint.

3. Warming Turmeric Latte

- Blend 1/2 teaspoon turmeric powder, 1 teaspoon honey, 1/2 cup warm milk (dairy or plant-based), and a pinch of black pepper.
- Top with cinnamon for added warmth and flavor.
- Turmeric boasts anti-inflammatory and mood-regulating properties, potentially easing aches and fatigue.

4. Cucumber & Melon Infused Water

- Slice cucumber and melon (watermelon, cantaloupe, etc.) and add them to a pitcher of water.
- Let infuse for at least 30 minutes for a lightly flavored and refreshing drink.
- Cucumbers offer hydration and potassium, while melons provide vitamins and antioxidants.

5. Ginger & Lemon Detox Tonic

- Muddle a few slices of fresh ginger in a glass.
- Squeeze in the juice of half a lemon and add warm water.
- Sweeten with honey or maple syrup (optional).
- Ginger aids digestion and has anti-inflammatory properties, potentially easing bloating and discomfort.

6. Berry Smoothie with Spinach

- Blend frozen berries, spinach, 1/2 cup yogurt (dairy or plant-based), and 1/2 cup liquid of your choice (milk, almond milk, coconut water).
- This nutrient-rich smoothie provides vitamins, minerals, and antioxidants, supporting overall well-being.

7. Golden Milk with Ashwagandha

- Warm 1 cup milk (dairy or plant-based) with 1/2 teaspoon turmeric powder, 1/4 teaspoon cinnamon, and a pinch of black pepper.

- Add 1/2 teaspoon ashwagandha powder (consult a doctor before using) for potential stress-reducing benefits.

- This comforting drink supports relaxation and sleep during PMDD fluctuations.

8. Herbal Tea Blend

- Combine calming herbs like valerian root, lavender, and lemon balm in a tea infuser.
- Steep in hot water for 5-10 minutes and enjoy a warm, fragrant brew.
- These herbs offer potential relaxation and stress-relieving properties, promoting inner peace.

9. Homemade Electrolyte Drink

- Mix 1/4 teaspoon sea salt, 1/8 teaspoon potassium bicarbonate, and a squeeze of lemon or lime juice in a glass of water.

- This DIY electrolyte drink helps replenish essential minerals, potentially combating fatigue and headaches.

10. Hibiscus & Rose Elixir

- Steep hibiscus flowers and dried rose petals in hot water for 5-10 minutes.
- Strain and let cool, adding a squeeze of honey or maple syrup for a touch of sweetness (optional).
- Hibiscus offers potential mood-boosting and anti-inflammatory benefits, while rose petals provide a delicate floral aroma and calming properties.
- This vibrant pink drink is not only hydrating but also visually appealing, offering a sensory reminder of self-care and inner peace.

Hydration Hero: Remember, staying hydrated throughout the day is crucial for managing PMDD symptoms. Aim for 8-10 glasses of water daily and adjust based on activity level and climate. Choose water-rich fruits and vegetables alongside these soothing beverages to amplify their effectiveness.

These are just a few ideas to get you started! Experiment with different flavors, combinations, and temperatures to find your perfect PMDD-calming beverage. Remember, staying mindful of your body's cues and prioritizing holistic self-care are key to navigating PMDD fluctuations with grace and resilience.

CHAPTER 10

Weekly Meal Plans for Your Menstrual Cycle: Fueling Each Phase with Flavor & Nourishment

Navigating your menstrual cycle through food can be a powerful tool for supporting optimal health and well-being. Here are four pre-designed weekly meal plans tailored to each phase, offering diverse options to suit your tastes and preferences:

1. Follicular Phase (Days 1-7)

This phase is about rebuilding and regeneration. Prioritize nutrient-rich foods to support hormonal balance and energy levels.

Monday

- **Breakfast:** Greek yogurt with berries and granola

- **Lunch:** Quinoa salad with roasted vegetables and chickpeas
- **Dinner:** Salmon with roasted sweet potato and green beans

Tuesday

- **Breakfast:** Scrambled eggs with spinach and tomatoes on whole-wheat toast
- **Lunch:** Lentil soup with whole-wheat bread
- **Dinner:** Turkey chili with brown rice

Wednesday

- **Breakfast:** Oatmeal with sliced almonds and bananas
- **Lunch:** Tuna salad sandwich on whole-wheat bread with avocado
- **Dinner:** Chicken stir-fry with brown rice and mixed vegetables

Thursday

- **Breakfast:** Smoothies with spinach, banana, and protein powder
- **Lunch:** Leftover chili
- **Dinner:** Vegetarian lasagna with lentil bolognese

Friday

- **Breakfast:** Scrambled tofu with bell peppers and onions on whole-wheat tortillas
- **Lunch:** Greek salad with grilled chicken or chickpeas
- **Dinner:** Shrimp scampi over whole-wheat pasta

Saturday

- **Breakfast:** Pancakes or waffles with fruit and nuts
- **Lunch:** Leftover salad or stir-fry

- **Dinner:** Date night! Choose a restaurant or cook a special meal you enjoy.

Sunday

- **Breakfast:** Brunch – French toast, eggs Benedict, or omelets
- **Lunch:** Leftovers or light salad
- **Dinner:** Roast chicken with roasted vegetables and mashed potatoes

2. Ovulatory Phase (Days 8-14)

This phase is about energy and increased appetite. Choose protein-rich foods to support ovulation and maintain satiety.

Monday

- **Breakfast:** Smoothie with Greek yogurt, berries, and protein powder

- **Lunch:** Chicken breast with quinoa and roasted vegetables
- **Dinner:** Lentil burgers on whole-wheat buns with sweet potato fries

Tuesday

- **Breakfast:** Eggs with avocado toast and smoked salmon
- **Lunch:** Tuna salad with mixed greens and whole-wheat crackers
- **Dinner:** Salmon with brown rice and asparagus

Wednesday

- **Breakfast:** Oatmeal with nuts and seeds
- **Lunch:** Leftover lentil burgers
- **Dinner:** Turkey stir-fry with brown rice and broccoli

Thursday

- **Breakfast:** Greek yogurt with granola and fruit

- **Lunch:** Chicken Caesar salad with whole-wheat bread

- **Dinner:** Vegetarian chili with cornbread

Friday

- **Breakfast:** Scrambled eggs with spinach and feta cheese on whole-wheat tortillas

- **Lunch:** Salmon salad sandwich on whole-wheat bread

- **Dinner:** Shrimp scampi over whole-wheat pasta

Saturday

- **Breakfast:** Pancakes or waffles with protein powder and nut butter

- **Lunch:** Leftover salad or chili

- **Dinner:** Steak or tempeh with baked sweet potato and green beans

Sunday

- **Breakfast:** Breakfast burrito with eggs, beans, and vegetables
- **Lunch:** Leftovers or light salad
- **Dinner:** Roast chicken with roasted vegetables and mashed potatoes

3. Luteal Phase (Days 15-28)

This phase is about preparing for your period. Choose anti-inflammatory and mood-boosting foods to combat PMS symptoms.

Monday

- **Breakfast:** Oatmeal with berries and chia seeds

- **Lunch:** Tuna salad with mixed greens and avocado
- **Dinner:** Salmon with roasted vegetables and quinoa

Tuesday

- **Breakfast:** Smoothie with spinach, banana, and protein powder
- **Lunch:** Lentil soup with whole-wheat bread
- **Dinner:** Chicken stir-fry with brown rice and mixed vegetables

Wednesday

- **Breakfast:** Greek yogurt with berries and granola
- **Lunch:** Leftover soup
- **Dinner:** Turkey chili with brown rice

Thursday

- **Breakfast:** Scrambled eggs with spinach and tomatoes on whole-wheat toast
- **Lunch:** Tuna salad sandwich on whole-wheat bread with avocado
- **Dinner:** Vegetarian lasagna with lentil bolognese

Friday

- **Breakfast:** Pancakes or waffles with fruit and nuts
- **Lunch:** Leftover salad or stir-fry
- **Dinner:** Date night! Choose a restaurant or cook a comforting meal you enjoy.

Saturday

- **Breakfast:** Scrambled tofu with bell peppers and onions on whole-wheat tortillas

- **Lunch:** Greek salad with grilled chicken or chickpeas
- **Dinner:** Chicken pot pie with whole-wheat crust

Sunday

- **Breakfast:** Brunch – French toast, eggs Benedict, or omelets
- **Lunch:** Leftovers or light salad
- **Dinner:** Roast chicken with roasted vegetables and mashed potatoes

Remember, these are just starting points! Feel free to mix and match meals from different phases, substitute ingredients to suit your dietary needs and preferences, and explore new options to keep your menu exciting. Here are some additional tips for building personalized meal plans:

1. **Tailor Portions:** Adjust portion sizes based on your activity level and individual needs. Listen to

your body's hunger cues and avoid overeating or restrictive dieting.

2. **Embrace Variety:** Include a colorful array of fruits, vegetables, whole grains, lean protein, and healthy fats in your meals to ensure you're getting a wide range of essential nutrients.

3. **Experiment with Flavors:** Don't shy away from spices and herbs! They add flavor and potential health benefits without adding unnecessary calories.

4. **Plan Snacks:** Having healthy snacks readily available can help prevent cravings and maintain energy levels throughout the day. Opt for fresh fruit, nuts, yogurt, or homemade trail mix.

5. **Cook at Home:** This gives you control over ingredients and allows you to tailor meals to your specific needs. However, don't feel guilty about enjoying the occasional takeout or restaurant meal!

6. **Stay Hydrated:** Water is crucial for overall health and plays a vital role in managing menstrual cycle symptoms. Aim for 8-10 glasses per day.

7. **Listen to Your Body:** Pay attention to how different foods make you feel. If you experience bloating, discomfort, or other negative reactions, adjust your meals accordingly.

8. **Make it Fun!:** Involve family and friends in meal planning and preparation. Enjoy cooking and eating together as a way to connect and nourish your body and soul.

Remember, your menstrual cycle is a natural and healthy part of being a woman. By supporting your body with delicious and nutritious foods, you can navigate each phase with grace, energy, and well-being.

This resource is just a starting point. I encourage you to continue exploring, modifying, and personalizing these meal plans to create a way of eating that truly empowers you on your menstrual cycle journey.

Bonus Tips

- Warm beverages like herbal teas and ginger honey water can be comforting and aid digestion.

- Incorporate anti-inflammatory herbs and spices like turmeric, ginger, and cinnamon into your meals.

- Stay hydrated with water and electrolyte-rich fluids.

- Don't hesitate to indulge in a comforting sweet treat once in a while, but choose options with good fats and natural sugars.

- Above all, prioritize rest and self-care during your menstrual phase. Listen to your body, delegate tasks if needed, and take time for activities that bring you peace and relaxation.

CHAPTER 11

Navigating PMDD with Grace: Embracing Holistic Healing and Self-Care

While PMDD symptoms can feel overwhelming, remember you have the power to reclaim your well-being through holistic approaches and mindful self-care practices. Here are some additional tips to support your journey:

Lifestyle Tweaks

1. **Move your body:** Exercise, even gentle walks or yoga, releases endorphins, reduces stress, and improves mood.

2. **Embrace nature:** Spending time outdoors boosts energy, decreases anxiety, and provides a sense of grounding.

3. **Prioritize sleep:** Aim for 7-8 hours of quality sleep each night to ensure hormonal balance and energy levels.

4. **Practice relaxation techniques:** Deep breathing, meditation, and progressive muscle relaxation can calm the mind and body.

5. **Connect with loved ones:** Social support plays a crucial role in emotional well-being.

6. **Seek professional help:** Don't hesitate to seek medical or therapeutic support for personalized guidance and treatment options.

Self-Care Rituals

1. **Mindful journaling:** Reflecting on your emotions and experiences can offer clarity and emotional release.

2. **Creative expression:** Painting, writing, dancing, or playing music can be powerful tools for emotional processing and stress relief.

3. **Warm baths or showers:** The physical warmth and sensory experience can soothe the mind and body.
4. Aromatherapy: Essential oils like lavender or chamomile can promote relaxation and stress reduction.

5. **Light candles or diffuse calming scents:** Create a spa-like atmosphere in your home to encourage relaxation.

6. **Set time for hobbies and activities that bring you joy:** Prioritize activities that nourish your soul and fill you with energy.

7. **Practice gratitude:** Focusing on the positive aspects of your life can shift your perspective and boost mood.

8. **Listen to your body:** Notice and honor your body's cues. Take breaks when needed, get enough sleep, and nourish yourself with healthy foods.

Remember: *Every woman experiences PMDD differently. Experiment with these suggestions and find what works best for you. Be patient with yourself, celebrate small victories, and embrace the journey of self-discovery and empowered well-being.*

You are not alone in this journey. We are a community of women committed to supporting each other on the path to holistic well-being and empowered lives.

Made in United States
Orlando, FL
30 December 2024